A Windsor
Correspondence

A Windsor Correspondence

BETWEEN

HRH The Duke of Edinburgh

AND

The Rt Rev Michael Mann

Dean of Windsor

with an Introduction by
LAUNCELOT FLEMING

Published for St George's House, Windsor Castle, 1984
by Michael Russell (Publishing) Ltd
The Chantry, Wilton, Salisbury, Wiltshire

Set in Sabon by The Spartan Press Ltd, Lymington
Printed and bound in Great Britain
by Biddles Ltd, Guildford, Dorking and King's Lynn

Contents

Introduction

Introduction

This correspondence came about as a result of Prince Philip sending Bishop Michael Mann, Dean of Windsor, a copy of Professor Sir Fred Hoyle's Omni Lecture which was delivered on 12 January 1982 under the title 'Evolution from Space', and asking for the Dean's comments. In his reply the Dean identified the main features of Professor Hoyle's thesis and indicated his fascination in the theory which Hoyle had propounded. He also raised points of objection from the Christian standpoint to some of the more speculative aspects of Hoyle's ideas. This set in train a lively interchange of letters which seemed of sufficient interest to merit publication – and, given the identity of the correspondents, nowhere more appropriately than as an occasional paper for St George's House.

St George's House, Windsor Castle, came into being in 1966 very largely on Prince Philip's initiative, ably supported and implemented by the then Dean of Windsor, Robin Woods. This Conference House was established to provide a place where men and women in positions of influence and responsibility, drawn from every area of society, might consider and evaluate current questions in which important value judgments are involved – this against the background of a Christian collegiate institution. It is also a place to which selected, and particularly senior, ministers and leaders of all Christian denominations are invited for in-service training courses to help provide them with a realistic relationship of their ministry to the modern world.

Ever since its establishment Prince Philip has taken a keen personal interest in the activities of the House and used it to probe and test out his own ideas, doubts and beliefs; and as the

Dean of Windsor is ex-officio Chairman of St George's House Council, it is with the present holder of this office that Prince Philip has shared many of his thoughts and questions on fundamental issues. The relationship between the two can be gauged not only from the character of this correspondence but also from Prince Philip's introduction to *A Question of Balance* in which he records his indebtedness to the Dean.

There is an intrinsic interest in a correspondence which reveals Prince Philip's questioning mind and deep concern about scientific and religious issues, and in the frank and able response of a sympathetic theologian and Christian apologist. But the subject matter of the correspondence also provides a stimulating commentary on certain aspects of Darwin's theory of evolution which has had such a profound and revolutionary influence on how man has come to see his own nature, his relationship with other forms of life and his understanding of religion. Darwin was not the first man to suggest that forms of life had evolved rather than been specially and separately created, but the publication in 1859 of *The Origin of Species* not only provided a wealth of evidence for the theory that animals and plants had in fact evolved, but also a credible theory as to how this had taken place.

The theory of evolution itself was and is widely accepted with the exception of a number of Creationists and Fundamentalists who adhere to a literal interpretation of the Bible and, in particular, of the description of the Creation given in the first chapters of Genesis. Darwin's theory as to how evolution happened – to use the original title of his book 'The Origin of Species by Means of Natural Selection, or the Preservation of Favoured Species in the Struggle for Life' – is however still contested by groups of mathematicians and biologists.

The Creationist campaign is very active especially in the southern states of the United States of America. From the evidence of this correspondence Prince Philip is evidently a target for their literature. One would be disposed to dismiss the Fundamentalist viewpoint as nonsensical but it evidently has a strong appeal to the followers of certain evangelical sects who sometimes defend their views with an arrogant vigour based on the conviction that they have a hot line to God which can brook no questioning.

The two main challenges to Darwin's theory as to how evolution has taken place deserve more serious attention. The biological challenge centres on the question as to how a new species splits off from its parentage. The Natural Selectionists' pin their faith on the view that if you allow a sufficiently long time to elapse, mutations within a species will accumulate in one particular direction sufficiently to allow the emergence of new species. But this process, however plausible, has not actually been demonstrated. All through the evolutionary record there are extraordinary leaps forward or moments when a number of changes seem to have appeared more or less simultaneously and it is difficult to understand precisely how these changes have developed. If, to quote an instance mentioned by Christopher Booker, you consider how an earthbound shrew evolved into a bat by growing a membrane between its fore and hind feet which turns into a wing, there must presumably have been a long intermediate stage between the first embryonic appearance of the membrane and its fully developed form as a wing 'when the unfortunate creature could neither run as efficiently as before or fly. In other words for a long period it must have been less fitted to survive rather than more' – a state of affairs contrary to the idea of survival of the fittest by natural selection.

The mathematical challenge to Darwin's theory of evolution is well illustrated by Sir Fred Hoyle in the Omni Lecture which has given rise to this correspondence. Hoyle points out the unlikelihood – indeed the near impossibility – of random mechanistic processes being responsible for organic evolution. The 200,000 amino-acid chains on which life depends could not, he asserts, have been obtained by random shuffling. Furthermore he argues that if evolution occurs in big jumps (which the existence of important missing links presupposes) the genetic potential for a jump must accumulate before the jump is made – i.e., before the consequences of the jump could become known. This would preclude the genetic changes being accumulated by natural selection – the changes would have to happen by chance. How a really big change of genetic material, not merely in amount but in structural organization, could occur simply – and by chance – quite defeats reasoned argument; or so it seems to Fred Hoyle. So Hoyle ascribes evolution and the production of new species to a cosmically driven process for acquiring new genes. On this hypothesis evolution is driven not from within, as has been the conventional view of biologists, but from without – the function of natural selection being not to create genetic possibilities (which it cannot do) but to decide which among a host of cosmic possibilities the local environment can support.

To support his hypothesis Hoyle demonstrates the existence of micro-organisms in space, taking as an example the meteorite which fell near Murchison, Australia in 1969 which contains carbonaceous-like material. He comes to the conclusion that biomaterials with their amazing measure of order must be the outcome, not of chance, but of intelligent design, and that if life is cosmic, intelligence must be cosmic too. At which point, and with Hoyle's observations of the relevance of what he has been saying to religion, the correspondence may be said 'to take off'.

Sir Fred Hoyle's lecture is a striking example of what is evident from an increasing number of scientists who, starting as agnostics or even atheists, as a result of their research are coming to the view that there must be some form of transcendent power (or, as Hoyle would call this, Intelligence) operating on and within the universe, and that certain scientific dilemmas call for a metaphysical explanation. This can help to dispel the damage which has been caused in the popular mind by the assumption that ultimately all the phenomena of life including human behaviour are open to explanation and understanding in terms of the sciences and their disciplines alone and that it is only a matter of time and further research that prevents full understanding and mastery. As a result religious belief, which of its very nature is not susceptible to such proofs, has either been restricted to a 'God of the gaps' or is not deemed worthy of consideration at all by enlightened minds.

At a time when the advances in science and technology have outstripped man's capacity for the moral control and use of the knowledge and power which such advances have placed in his hands, it is all the more necessary that the scientist and theologian can each come to recognize the areas within which their disciplines apply and what conclusions can properly be drawn, and those areas within which they are inapplicable or irrelevant, and so be able to assess each other's contributions to an understanding of the world and the meaning of life.

As the Dean says, in the Easter sermon which has been included in this correspondence, scientific truth and religious truth are complementary not opposed; and since science and theology have become more aware of their limitations, they have both started to show a humility which is helping to create an atmosphere where mutual support becomes possible. In such an atmosphere the scientific experience and the aesthetic and religious experience can be integrated into a richer vision of life and its purposes. Catherine Roberts has said: 'A truer , more holistic vision of the universe and its different levels of reality requires insight that can relate science to questions of good and evil and final cause. Nor can scientific investigation long survive without a more fully developed conscience.' Both science and religion need liberation. This correspondence, with its searching and undogmatic approach, is a stimulating contribution to that end.

LAUNCELOT FLEMING

Evolution

Evolution

Sir,

I was fascinated to read Professor Fred Hoyle's Omni Lecture which you so thoughtfully sent me.

As I understand the paper, Fred Hoyle is expressing a belief in a form of evolution by natural selection operating upon mutations which are generated by some form of directed intelligence, and not by chance. Hoyle dismisses the 'chance evolutionists' by demonstrating the mathematical improbability of any reconciliation between their devotion to both random selection and some form of rational mechanism. He underlines his argument by demonstrating the way in which the nature of the evolutionary process seems to be clearly subject to some form of direction. As Hoyle points out, there are just too many 'missing links' for this random evolutionary position to be logically tenable. Up to this point we all go along with Hoyle, and in fact this is the position which has been adopted by many Christians once they overcame the initial shock of Darwinism, and when they sought to come to terms with a theory of evolution.

Hoyle then propounds a new theory that the process of evolution started outside our planet from the solar system, and that it is influenced by a perpetual bombardment of Earth by micro-organisms from space. This is a fascinating proposition, which sounds entirely possible, and which surely must be proved or disproved in the fairly near future, given the scientific evidence which must become available in the foreseeable future. We remain fascinated and interested, but probably agnostic at this stage of the evidence.

The third aspect of Hoyle's paper is much more speculative and open to criticism from the Christian standpoint. He suggests that if life is cosmic, then intelligence must be cosmic too. He then goes on to suggest a pre-existent intelligence, which propagates itself 'as a matter of stark necessity' and survival. It does this by means of an 'immense technology' creating carbonaceous life, and propagating itself forward from earlier physical conditions which were being rendered untenable, by means of varying forms of 'soft ware'. His analogy is that our human bodies are the 'hard ware', and our intelligence is the 'soft ware'. He further suggests that if, for some cataclysmic reasons, *homo sapiens* were to cease to exist, the pre-existent intelligence would, as a matter of survival, find some other form of 'soft ware' by which to perpetuate itself.

To the Christian this is surely open to two objections. First, Hoyle is merely removing the essential problem another stage backwards. How did the pre-existent intelligence evolve? Is Hoyle suggesting a theory of continuous creation, of one pre-existent intelligence being created by a previous one ad infinitum? This would necessitate a universe that is infinitely old, but Hoyle himself acknowledges that a theory of infinite age is unconvincing. And how could he reconcile such a theory with the 'Big Bang' idea, which seems to command a great deal of scientific support?

Secondly, although the paper as a whole adopts a 'holist' approach, this particular line of thought is too reductionist for me. In the beginning, what? For me the first four words of Genesis remain the only convincing answer – 'In the beginning God'. Hoyle's theory does not attempt to face the human dilemma about life itself. What is the point of human life? Is death the end? If it is, then, as St Paul says – 'We are of all men the most miserable.' Man, since his beginning, has sought the answer to the reason for his life, and to the riddle of his death. Hoyle sidesteps this crucial issue altogether. Man cannot live without hope, and the only theory that has satisfied me is that God became man in Jesus Christ, who conquered death and gave us the hope of eternal life. Without that hope, life becomes a sorry mockery of what it should be, and we are left with the selfish and demeaning pessimism of 'eat, drink and be merry, for tomorrow we die'.

Finally, what is so encouraging to the Christian about this paper is that science itself now seems to be moving towards a much more 'holist' view of existence, and away from reductionism. An atmosphere is being created which is much more compatible with the Christian point of view. Science and Christianity seem to be moving towards each other, where previously they have too often been seen to be in opposition to each other. And this is very, very exciting, especially when a paper like this comes from a cosmologist, well known for his past atheism!

MICHAEL MANN

Dear Michael,

I was intrigued to know how you would react.

I agree that the idea of bombardment of the Earth by micro-organisms from space would help to explain a number of anomalies but, as you say, it merely pushes Divine intervention a bit further back.

Having said that, I must take issue with you on some of your other points. It seems to me that the argument between Darwin and creation has taken place because churchmen have felt that while God, according to Genesis, invented creation – and therefore they had to defend it – Darwin somehow 'invented' evolution. In fact all that Darwin did was to show that God had invented the process of evolution which achieved the same result but over a longer period of time. Once you accept this then there is nothing 'chancy' about evolution because presumably God foresaw the outcome and the eventual appearance of man. Incidentally, Hoyle's mathematical improbability depends entirely on the choice of parameters. He would probably be right in the case of total stability in all external factors, but probably wrong where the external factors are unstable and highly variable.

[19]

I am not enthusiastic about pre-existent intelligence and I find it a bit too far-fetched to accept that bombarding the earth with micro-organisms is a likely way of ensuring survival. Survival of what? On the other hand, I cannot get worked up about the point of human life and I certainly don't agree with your alternative of 'eat, drink and be merry, etc.'. Whatever the point of human life the fact remains that human civilization has existed for very many generations and, barring accidents (due to too much eating, drinking, and being merry, no doubt), there is every likelihood that human life will go on for many generations in the future. If we didn't believe that, why procreate? Consequently, the point of life is the attempt to make it more tolerable and more civilized for the generations we have every reason to believe will live after us. Whether 'God became man in Jesus Christ' is a philosophical question; what is a matter of fact is that Jesus tried to show us how to live so that the world would become a better place.

I am glad you think science and Christianity are moving closer together, but that is not quite the point. The problem is that the breach between science and theology will remain just as wide as long as the Bible is used as the authority for the explanation of natural phenomena which is at variance with scientific fact or with scientific theory that meets all known facts.

PHILIP

Sir,

The argument between Darwin and the Church took place because, up to 1859 when Darwin published his *Origin of the Species*, Christians had accepted that the Bible was a literal account of factual events and Darwin's thesis seemed to attack what had previously been accepted without question. A hundred and twenty years later, only those Christians who are Fundamentalists would wish to ascribe literal truth to the Bible. It is now seen as having been written by men who were conditioned in their thinking, as much as we are, within the limitations of the particular epoch in which they lived. But this is not to go to the other extreme and say that the Bible is nonsense. In fact Darwin's challenge has helped us to a much better understanding of the Scriptures as conveying spiritual truth, which is not always synonomous with literal truth, and should be seen more in the sense of poetry and as truth conveyed through story and parable. The break between science and theology will remain just as wide as long as scientists still imagine that theologians are stuck in a position which they ceased to hold years ago. Theologians have not used the Bible as the authority for the explanation of natural phenomena for decades, and to imagine they do is to be completely out of touch with contemporary theological thought. Theology has had to relearn from science that it is a dynamic and not a static discipline. So I am still optimistic and excited about the future relationship of science and theology.

I agree with what you say about evolution. I was using the word 'chance' in respect of evolution in the sense that anything that is 'random' is 'chancy'.

It is not only evolution but the mechanics of evolution which Darwin suggested were solely due to the random mutations of genetic material, or to the variations of the principle of survival of the fittest. Surely this makes the idea of 'chance' fundamental to Darwin? If – and I agree it is a big 'if' – Hoyle's mathematics are right, where does this leave Darwin? Darwin himself saw clear indications of 'design' in the process of evolution, but was not convinced that this was or was not an argument for the existence of God. What is encouraging to the Christian is that if, as he does, he has other reasons for believing in God, then the evidence of design from scientists is encouraging.

Where I might place a different emphasis is when you say: 'The point of life is the attempt to make it more tolerable and more civilized for the generations we have every reason to believe will live after us.' That is, in the Christian view, only part of the point. The belief that 'God became man in Jesus Christ' is not, in the Christian view, a philosophical question; it is a matter of faith. And to say that 'Jesus tried to show us how to live so that the world would become a better place' is to be selective of the evidence and to ignore the main thrust of the New Testament. If Jesus was merely a fine ethical teacher, I doubt whether the New Testament would have been written, and certainly not in the way it has come down to us. New Testament accounts support the view that what turned his most trusted followers from the cowardice they showed on Good Friday to the reckless courage of a few weeks later was that they, at any rate, believed that Jesus had risen from the dead. Jesus also told them that his kingdom was *not* of this world. The courage of the ordinary folk who made up the early Christian martyrs (on contemporary Roman evidence) was that they believed in a life to come after death. Time and again Jesus warned his disciples that we shall be accountable for our deeds in this world at some stage beyond death. Of course what happens in this world is vitally important, but part of its importance is because it is set in a much wider context than life here and now.

There is another reason why I believe it to be wrong to say that the point of life is only to make it better for future generations. The Christian believes that all men are of equal value in the eyes of God. Therefore it follows that it must be wrong to look upon our forbears as mere stepping stones to the present, and ourselves as stepping stones to the future?

In addition to the Christian hope for the future, there is another sense in which he is also meant to live for the present 'redeeming the time'. This comes through very clearly in the New Testament. We live the present to the full in hope for the future, and what we have and are is largely by the endeavours of the past. So to the Christian time is an interwoven fabric of past, present and future.

MICHAEL MANN

Dear Michael,

First, your point about chance and random. Let me just quote the last paragraph of *The Origin of Species*:

It is interesting to contemplate a tangled bank, clothed with many plants of many kinds, with birds singing on the bushes, with various insects flitting about, and with worms crawling through the damp earth, and to reflect that these elaborately constructed forms, so different from each other, and dependent upon each other in so complex a manner, have all been produced by laws acting around us. These laws, taken in the largest sense being Growth with Reproduction; Inheritance which is almost implied by reproduction; Variability from the indirect and direct action of the conditions of life and from use and disuse; a Ratio of Increase so high as to lead to a struggle for Life, and as a consequence to Natural Selection, entailing Divergence of Character and the Extinction of less-improved forms. Thus from the war of nature, from famine and death, the most exalted object which we are capable of conceiving, namely, the production of the higher animals, directly follows. There is grandeur in this view of life, with its several powers, which have been originally breathed by the Creator into a few forms, or only one, and that whilst this planet has gone cycling on according to the fixed laws of gravity, from so simple a beginning endless forms most beautiful and most wonderful have been and are being evolved.

No reference, you will note, to chance or random selection. The point is that selection is made by a great many influences over a very long period of time.

As to the point of life, I think you are equating 'faith' with action. As you say, the Apostles lost their cowardice because of their faith, consequently their faith influenced their actions.

You say yourself that Jesus warned his disciples that we shall be accountable for *our deeds in this world*, which implies to me that the quality of life after death depends absolutely on our actions in this world. In other words it is not the degree of our faith for which we are accountable, but our actions. Frankly I cannot see any criterion for acceptable actions unless they are based on Christ's teaching which I understand to be intended

[23]

to benefit future generations. I would prefer to follow his teaching because I am convinced that it is right, than simply as a means of getting a better deal in Heaven. Furthermore, I *know* about this world while I have to rely on my faith for a very incomplete understanding of the next.

I don't see anything wrong or un-Christian about being a 'stepping stone' to the future. We cannot help it anyway. The point is that we should be stepping stones to a better future.

PHILIP

Sir,

I think that to a certain extent we may be arguing along parallel lines.

As I have already said, the theory of evolution holds no threat to modern theological thought. Whatever Darwin himself said, Darwinists appear to have reached the stage today where they seem to claim that natural selection is a random process. But again a lot depends upon what is meant by 'random' or 'chance'. Darwin in his final paragraph is talking of 'the Creator' with a capital 'C', and yet he held that his theory neither proved nor disproved the existence of God.

My only other comment is that, to Anglican thought, justification by works alone is inadequate. Throughout the Gospels Jesus said to people – 'Thy faith has made thee whole.' Faith is as pointless without works, as are works without faith. Faith influences actions, but actions derive from faith. Both are complementary and necessary. We shall therefore be accountable for both faith and deeds. Without faith, like Peter, we sink. Without deeds, we are hypocrites. Of course you are right to say that we follow Christ's teaching because it is right, not because it is some form of stick and carrot for a better deal hereafter. But to suggest that is to destroy the balance of what I was trying to say. Why do actions in this world have to be limited to the benefit of future generations? Of course that is right, but why cannot, in addition, the hope of life after death for you and me be part of the total concept? We are what we are by virtue of those who have gone before us; we live our lives in gratitude for their good endeavours, and so that we in our turn may add to those endeavours for those to come. When our own turn to die comes, it is with the hope and the promise that in some way we do not understand, and although we shall be accountable for our good and bad deeds, our soul will live on, and that our spirit will join with those whom we have loved in what we call the Communion of Saints. That concept involves past, present and future.

To end with Darwin's own words: 'There is a grandeur in this view of life.'

MICHAEL MANN

Dear Michael,

I did not mean to imply that evolution holds a threat to *modern* theological thought. I was merely suggesting a reason why evolution caused such a problem in the first place. I then went on to suggest that evolution provides for that essential flexibility necessary for life to survive on earth. My contention, therefore, is that it is not simply that evolution is no threat but that what is described as the Creation was in fact the process of evolution that was established by God.

However that may be, I would be interested to know how modern theological thought copes with *homo sapiens*. Is he part of the process of evolution or is he an exception; and if so, what sort of exception?

I am sure that there can be no such thing as faith without works, but I find it very hard to accept that there can be no good works without faith, although I suppose it depends on what you mean by good works and faith. If acts of altruism are good then there is evidence that even certain animals are capable of good works. On the other hand, if works can only be good if they are the consequence of faith in Christ then that excludes a very large proportion of mankind and is a little discouraging for those Christians whose faith is perhaps not sufficiently fully developed to be able to comprehend the concept of eternal life.

As to the Christian faith, would it be fair to describe it as faith in as much of Christ's teaching as it is possible to comprehend? For some it may encompass the promise of eternal life, for others it may get no further than trying to act according to his teaching.

In your original letter you said 'Without that hope [of eternal life] life becomes a mockery etc.', which seems to imply that the hope of eternal life should be the only motivation or justification for life. Surely if you have absolute faith, eternal life is not a matter of hope but of certainty. The only point of doubt is the quality of that eternal life, as I would assume that it depends upon the quality of the works done in this life. At the moment I can think of no other measure for the quality of works than that they be for the benefit of present and future generations, including the possibility of giving up life itself. All of which seems to have brought me back to where I started.

PHILIP

Sir,

I think I am in complete agreement with your contention about evolution. I do not think that the problem of *homo sapiens* vis-à-vis creation is a major one to theological thought. If *homo sapiens* is a part of evolution (and the existing evidence is so strong as to indicate that he is), then the theologian must examine how this affects God's part in such evolution. My guess would be that it does not make much difference, once one has accepted that evolution is a process established by God.

The Christian doctrine of the Incarnation, that God became

[26]

homo sapiens in the person of Jesus, is not contingent upon the doctrine of Creation. At the particular time that this happened, *homo sapiens* was in a particular state of evolution, which made this act the way God chose to take. We believe that God chose to act in that way at that time.

Good works are not dependent upon Christian faith – to state that would be to fly in the face of a vast amount of evidence. All I am trying to say is that for those who consider themselves to be Christians, faith is an essential element. I do not think it is adequate to say that faith is 'as much of Christ's teaching as it is possible to comprehend'. The writer of Hebrews describes faith as 'the assurance of things hoped for, the proving of things not seen'. It seems to me that the essential element of faith, in its theological sense, is the belief in things which cannot necessarily be proved in the scientific sense of proof, but which is sufficiently strong to provide the motivation to action. It is believing in those things which are not subject to scientific analysis. I cannot prove eternal life, but I believe in it, on the basis of the spiritual evidence, and in humble awareness that it is, for me, through Jesus Christ that I do so believe.

Certainly the hope of eternal life is not the *only* justification for life. The benefit of good works to present and future generations is a major element, as you rightly point out. But as I have said before, it does not end there; justification by works is important, but by itself it is not enough. There is also the motivation that after this life we shall be answerable for the way in which we have behaved, and that after death our spirit is not extinguished like a candle, but somehow, in some way which we do not fully understand, that it lives on.

But having stated my faith, I am very aware that others may not feel able to share it, and for those who cannot take that 'step in the dark', the Christian can only honour their doubt with the deepest and most sympathetic and affectionate understanding.

MICHAEL MANN

Fundamentalism and Creation

Fundamentalism and Creation

Dear Michael,

Somebody sent me this book from the United States [Wilder-Smith's *Man's Origin, Man's Destiny*]. Apparently there has been quite a revival of Fundamentalism in the States and a reversion from Darwin to Genesis. This book sets out the case. I cannot say I find it convincing, particularly as he seems to argue that as he believes that Darwin was wrong, therefore Genesis must be right. I do not think that follows at all!

He does not appear to notice that many of his arguments against Darwin are equally valid against Genesis.

There is quite an interesting section about pain and suffering. He derides Darwin for rejecting God because he could not believe that God could have created a system that involved so much cruelty. Then he goes on to suggest that God was only the 'designer' and not responsible for the way nature works. After all, creation or evolution – the end result in nature as we know it is the same! And whatever we might like to think, nature is the way it is.

He makes an interesting analogy about fossil motor cars but then goes and draws all the wrong conclusions. The car did, evolve by a process of the commercial survival of the fittest and although each model had its own designer there was no single designer for the whole process – except perhaps the 'market'. Perhaps that is where he thinks God is?

PHILIP

Sir,

I am deeply suspicious of the Fundamentalism that is now rampant in the States, and I believe that it is a retreat by

[31]

frightened people to a form of authoritarianism, which denies our bounden duty to follow truth wherever it may lead. The trouble with Fundamentalists is that they tend to select those aspects of truth that fit their theories, and to ignore any awkward points. After all, if you have an exclusive 'hot line' to God, and God speaks to you directly, who may contradict? It all lapses too easily into a form of spiritual arrogance and dictatorship. Theologians, like scientists, have got to go on learning humility, and to follow truth wherever it may lead, in the faith that it will increase, and not diminish, their vision and understanding of God.

I am taking the liberty of including a copy of my Easter sermon, as it is really a part of our correspondence on this subject.

MICHAEL MANN

[Enclosure]

'Jesus Christ is risen today.'

In 1859 Charles Darwin published his *Origin of Species*. Its effect was dramatic. To many the theory of evolution seemed to make nonsense of the stories in Genesis, and to cast doubt upon the truth and reliability of the Bible. The position was not helped by the reaction of the religious establishment. In a famous encounter the then Bishop of Oxford, Wilberforce – known less affectionately as 'Soapy Sam' – took on the redoubtable Professor T. H. Huxley in public, and got very much the worst of the encounter. The further discoveries of science over the next hundred years, and the advent of Freud and the social sciences, seemed to widen this gap between rational thought and religious belief, which was often wrongly depicted as being based on a blind acceptance of discredited myths.

The scientific method was in its heyday. New knowledge allied to technological advance gave a combination by which each fed on the other, until nothing seemed to be beyond man's eventual capability and grasp. Science and reason would prevail. All this was given enormous political stimulus by the theories of Karl Marx. Many who hated Communism began to wonder whether perhaps religion was 'the opium of the people' after all. Many of the most rational and intelligent of people felt bound to remain agnostic and materialism unsupported by spiritual values was able to flourish, fed by the extraordinary benefits of technology.

But there were clouds, no bigger than a man's hand, on the horizon which were in turn to shake this new-found confidence that man, in spite of the odd setback, was steadily moving towards his own self-made Utopia. That confident society that gave birth to Darwin, Freud and Marx was shattered by the events of 1914–18. And afterwards the 'world fit for heroes' did not materialize. Instead there was Depression, and from it arose the satanic evil of Hitler and Stalin and all the calculated inhuman cruelty that has followed.

What had science and technology to say about this? For it was science and technology that made poison gas available with such efficiency; that enabled evil men to devise horrific new methods of torture; that provided the means whereby good men and true were pushed into using nuclear power – not to warm our homes and drive our factories, but to act as an agent of mass obliteration. Now it was the turn of the scientists to be defensive. 'We merely pursue knowledge wherever it leads; it is up to the rest of you how you use it.' But confidence in the faith which created the morality, which should have gone hand in hand with the scientific method, had been undermined by it. The new knowledge had, in Britain, helped to form a generation of agnostics, who did not know what they believed, and did not worry overmuch so long as they were comfortable and were not disturbed. Many agnostics are the most moral of individuals, but unfortunately agnosticism does little to sustain corporate morality. There was created a religious vacuum which the material growth of recent years

[33]

sustained until the mid-seventies. The only morality that seemed to command acceptance was what you could get away with is what is acceptable.

But a new climate is emerging. Science is concerned with measurable fact, and we are having to relearn that even science has its limitations. It cannot measure the beauty of a sunset, or the pleasure of a deep friendship. When a young person is killed, or a dearly loved relative dies, science cannot help us in our grief and our sense of powerlessness and frustration. Science cannot tell us the right and the wise way to use the new options it keeps on offering to us. As crime rates soar, and some of our young indulge in mugging and vandalism, science has not provided a social discipline or a sense of purpose that will satisfy these frustrations. We are rediscovering that it is religious conviction alone that seems capable of sustaining the integrity and the dignity of the individual. It is not that the religious way is superior to the scientific, or vice versa. They both pursue Truth. For Truth cannot be separated; scientific truth and religious truth are complementary, not opposed. And as both science and theology have become more aware of their limitations, they have both started to show a humility, which is helping to create an atmosphere where mutual support becomes possible. It is said of Devonshire people 'that they are all for truth, but don't like to be too dogmatic about it'. Not a bad motto for scientists and theologians.

The religious way is the way of faith – of knowing something to be right or true in yourself. A Beethoven symphony may move you deeply. No one can prove to you why you thought it so beautiful. But you *know* that it was so for you. It is the way of intuition.

Those early disciples *knew* that Jesus Christ had conquered death. They saw him die, and they had helped to bury the corpse. They then had this extraordinary experience, which transformed their previous cowardice and disillusion into faith – they walked and talked with someone they knew to be that dead Jesus. Afterwards in trying to describe it, they were at a

[34]

loss for words; it was so beyond any normal human experience. But they knew it had happened. And this conviction was so strong that even St Paul, who was not one of them, later wrote that those who could not believe were 'of all men the most miserable'.

To the agnostic the argument of faith can be irritating, because if it is true it is unanswerable, and yet it is not open to proof by scientific methods. In my experience women very often have this intuitive sense more highly developed than men. My wife will sometimes say to me – 'I don't know what it is about that person, I can't put my finger on it, but there is something that is not quite right.' And thirty-three years of marriage have taught me to pay careful heed to such intuitive feelings! This is something of the way in which faith operates; we see God working through the lives of other people, and we experience that power in ourselves. We know it.

Today is Easter Day – Jesus Christ is risen today. That is our faith our hope that our God became as *you* and *me* in the man Jesus; that he lived and died as we must do. *But* he conquered death, and gave us the hope that death is not the end. We test that hope by our own experience of faith.

'Jesus Christ is risen today.'

Dear Michael,

Thank you for lending me *The Emerging Order* [by Jeremy Rifkin and Ted Howerd]. I found it fascinating reading and deeply worrying. There is no doubt that conservation is a moral issue but I really do not see how it can be helped by the reactionary Fundamentalist philosophy propounded in the book. The worst part is the way various scientific doctrines and the laws of thermodynamics are misinterpreted to apply to situations to which they were never intended to apply.

Perhaps the most surprising idea is that a new interpretation of 'dominion over all living things' is going to fuel a new reformation.

I am quite sure that a very large proportion of thinking people have always understood 'dominion over' to mean 'responsibility for'; otherwise why are there any conservationists? To suggest that the whole 'development' ethic of the last 200 years is due to a different understanding of the word 'dominion' in Genesis, is really much too simplistic. However, I do concede that materialism has very definitely been encouraged by its own success and that this has had important consequences on moral standards, political philosophies and religious beliefs. I certainly hope that the evident difficulties we are now getting into will encourage more people to recognize that religion and morality must play more important parts in future ambitions and plans; but not, I fervently hope, under the terms set out in this book.

PHILIP

Sir,

I was most interested to read your comments on *The Emerging Order*, with which I wholly agree. As I said, the book is an exposure of the Fundamentalist position, and I believe it can be used to demonstrate the dangers inherent in that stance. As you point out, the arguments used are simplistic in the extreme – but this is a trait of the Fundamentalists, and thus the approach is very attractive to frightened and confused people looking for spiritual security.

Man's Origin, Man's Destiny is perhaps more sophisticated in its manner, but because of this it cloaks the real nature of Fundamentalism, whereas *The Emerging Order* is more stark. It is a very worrying and frightening trend, and is reviving now in England.

Fundamentalism, by its very nature, tends to be authoritarian and intolerant of any argument that does not fit into its own scheme of things. After all, if the Bible is thought to be literally true and not open to question, and if you have 'a hot line to God' – who may question or contradict, for that would

[36]

be blasphemy? It is this arrogance and intolerance that I find most objectionable, and most contrary to the spirit of humility, which I believe to be the hallmark of proper theological inquiry.

Another danger lies in the tendency for every action to breed a reaction. If Fundamentalism does grow in Britain – and there are signs that it may do so – then we need to be careful also about the inevitable reaction to it, or we could see a drift towards extreme points of view. This trend has occurred in other disciplines, and it would set back the search for truth in the spiritual sphere if it were to happen to theology.

You may have seen the attached article which appeared in *The Times*, when you were in Canada and the United States. In case you missed it, I thought it might be of interest.

MICHAEL MANN

[Abridged from *The Times*, 19 April 1982]

THE DESCENT OF DARWIN
100 YEARS ON

CHRISTOPHER BOOKER

Darwin is of course best known as the thinker who provided scientifically-minded modern man with an acceptable answer to the age-old question 'where did man come from?' In the popular mind he is firmly identified as the originator of the theory of evolution – the man who courageously defied the established view of the ages by insisting that we are descended from monkeys.

The truth, however, is rather more complicated. In no sense was Darwin the founder of the theory of evolution. Naturalists had been suggesting that life forms had evolved, rather than been specially and separately created, for 70 years before the publication of Darwin's *Origin of Species* in 1859.

[37]

What Darwin did was to synthesize and to develop with great power a number of ideas which had been floating in the air for some time.

The essence of Darwin's theory was this: every form of life displays countless minute natural variations (which may be rapidly and vastly exaggerated by the kind of artificial selection which gives rise to different breeds of dogs or pansies). Some of these variations may be more fitted to assist their owners to survive than others, and therefore their descendants will be the ones who do survive.

Over long periods of geological time, these more adapted forms will split off and become new species (like Darwin's Galapagos finches), and this is how the forms of life have ascended the ladder of creation, from the protozoon to *homo sapiens.*

It was a beautifully simple and attractive theory. The only trouble was that, as Darwin himself was at least partly aware, it was full of colossal holes.

One was that, if evolution has been a continuous process, why does the fossil record only show us apparently settled and established species, each readily identifiable? Why does it not include an abundance of intermediate forms? Darwin's reiterated answer to this was only that the fossil record is 'highly imperfect' – i.e. that when we found more fossils we should find the evidence to support his theory.

Another serious problem was that Darwin based much of his theory on his knowledge of the astonishing variations which may be obtained in almost any form of life by artificial selection. But although breeding may give us two creatures as apparently unalike as a Great Dane and a Chihuahua, the fact is that they both remain members of the same species, *canis familiaris* or dog, capable of interbreeding (and if by any miracle they can be persuaded to do so, there is nothing to ensure that their descendants will not revert to being just common-or-garden mongrels).

In other words, we have here the supreme irony that a book which has become famous for explaining the origin of species in fact does nothing of the kind. Whatever else Darwin's book may have achieved, it does not explain the still utterly mysterious process whereby a life form develops across that barrier which marks the emergence of a clearcut new species, no longer capable of making fertile crosses with members of the species from which it developed.

Of course, in our own century the followers of Darwin, or Neo-

Darwinians, have made tremendous play with discoveries in genetics, and in particular with genetic mutations. It is on this that the Natural Selectionists now hang their faith to account for the major leaps forward in the evolutionary story, and on the belief that if you somehow allow for a long enough lapse of time, mutations within a species will accumulate in one particular direction sufficiently to allow for the 'splitting off' of a new species. But alas, it has to be urged on such rational, scientific minds that belief is not quite the same thing as actual demonstration.

Indeed we have here what is perhaps the most insurmountable problem of all. All through the evolutionary record there are extraordinary 'leaps forward', or moments when all sorts of benevolent changes seem to have appeared more or less simultaneously.

In the popular television series *Life on Earth*, David Attenborough sought to demonstrate the miracle of natural selection by showing how an earthbound shrew evolved into a bat by growing a membrane between its fore and hind feet which turned into a wing.

But how, according to the process of natural selection, could such a thing conceivably have happened? There must have been a long intermediate stage between the first embryonic appearance of the membrane and its fully developed form as a wing, when the unfortunate creature could neither run as efficiently as before nor fly. In other words, for a long period it must have been *less* fitted to survive rather than more – so how and why did it happen? Certainly not according to any process remotely recognizable as Darwinian (or Neo-Darwinian) natural selection.

The truth is that a century after Darwin's death, we still have not the slightest demonstrable or even plausible idea of how evolution really took place – and in recent years this has led to an extraordinary series of battles over the whole question.

On the one hand, particularly in the United States, there has been a remarkable revival in old-fashioned biblical Fundamentalism, in the belief that evolution did not take place at all – that somehow Genesis was literally right and that God created the world and every species in it pretty well simultaneously.

On the other hand, a state of almost open war has broken out among the evolutionists themselves, with every kind of sect urging some new modification to Darwin, or 'retreat' into Lamarckianism – or even into a new approach called 'cladistics' which may best be summed up as the semiology, or structuralism of biology, a last forlorn refuge of man the insatiable classifier.

What does not seem to have occurred to more than a handful of people is to urge that life on earth *has* evolved, from simple forms to complex – but that, as to how and why it really happened, we have not the slightest idea and probably never shall. It will simply remain God's secret.

Dear Michael,

I was very interested to read Booker's article on Darwin. I think he is right in the first part, that Darwin synthesized and developed existing ideas, but I think he underestimates the force of the theory put together by Darwin. In the first place, Darwin was fully aware that the theory appeared to be 'full of holes'. In fact, he devotes more space in *Origin* to dealing with Booker's objections than to the theory itself.

The one case chosen by Booker of the interbreeding of Great Dane and Chihuahua is, ironically, a good example of varieties within a species diverging to such an extent that they are unable to make a fertile cross.

I sympathize with your views on Fundamentalism, but what is the alternative theological position? You appear to agree with Hoyle's and Booker's doubts about Darwin, yet you imply that evolution is a more likely explanation than creation. Or to put it another way, the Fundamentalists make their position quite clear; what exactly is the position of those who are not Fundamentalists? I don't think 'don't know' is an acceptable answer!

Incidentally, I would be interested to know how the Fundamentalist accounts for God's intention to drown His creation in the Flood. If Adam was the cause for the 'Fall from Grace', why did God believe that Noah's descendants would do any better? And why save all the animals when he could have easily recreated them all again?

PHILIP

[40]

Sir,

To revert to *Man's Origin, Man's Destiny*. The first part I find a waste of time. But then I have no patience with the Fundamentalist who tries to make the Bible a literal explanation of scientific fact. In the first place I do not believe that the Bible was meant to be so interpreted: much of it is a later writing down of a much earlier oral tradition, and all of it was written by men confined within the limitations of their own epoch. The Bible speaks in terms of a spiritual truth, although these spiritual truths of the Bible are grounded and illustrated by the experience of God at work in individual lives at various times. Secondly, I cannot see that literal interpretations of Adam and Eve, or of the Flood, get us anywhere. For me these are traditions set in poetic form, probably based on folk memory, but expressing great spiritual truths rather than literal fact.

Man is different from other living species in that he possesses these spiritual faculties. No matter how the world was created or came into being, or if it evolved, we still need an explanation of the spiritual side of man. The Bible is saying that God is spirit, and man must worship Him in spirit and in truth. To me this means that religion is concerned with why we do things more than how we do them. It is concerned with happiness and fulfilment, with pain and suffering, with life and death, with right and wrong – in fact with all the things of the human spirit. But it is also concerned with truth, and therefore it must follow truth, wherever truth leads, in the faith that God is truth and therefore trust will lead me to a better understanding of God. So if scientists prove some new fact, we have as Christians to accept that fact, and apply it to our knowledge of God. But Fundamentalists start at the other end, they take the Bible and test proven facts against the Bible. The Bible was never meant to be so used. And that sort of argument reduces religion to the medieval exercise of arguing how many angels can stand on the head of a pin!

I am much more in sympathy when he deals with death and

the sanctity of the individual and the fact that lack of observation proves nothing. But again I part company with him over his extraordinary arrogance over 'born again Christians' and the special privileges which are to be theirs.

The early religious opposition to the theory of evolution was based upon a traditional and to my mind an erroneous belief in the literal truth of scripture. The main service that Darwin performed for religious truth was to free its proponents from a literal slavery, and to teach them afresh that truth must be followed by Christians wherever it leads. The religious opposition to Darwin was profoundly misplaced. But that is not to go to the other extreme and say that Darwin's theory of evolution is true. But because it is ethically netural, in that it does not, or should not, affect the religious standpoint, theology should remain ethically neutral until the scientists have enough evidence to make a considered judgment.

If Darwin forced theologians back to theology, and away from unthinking prejudice, he also performed another service. In following truth wherever it leads, he did enable Christians to catch a glimpse of a much wider and greater vision of God than had been previously vouchsafed to them. When we oppose truth, we diminish ourselves and our view of God. When we accept it humbly and follow it, even when it may seem at first to shatter our belief, it does (once we can see it in perspective) in fact enrich and deepen our faith and understanding.

MICHAEL MANN

Science and Religious
Conservatism

Science and Religious Conservatism

Dear Michael,

I apologize for talking rather a lot at the meeting of the Council of St George's House, particularly about the future of the Church, but I had an idea that most members might be inhibited by what is a pretty daunting subject and I thought a few ideas might spark some response.

On reflection one or two other points have come to mind. I am a bit surprised that I did not bring up my hobby-horse – the need to reconcile science and theology. I still think this is the crux of much of the problem. Perhaps it is a mistake to try to achieve a reconciliation by dialogue with scientists. It might be better to get theologians to discuss theology in the context of scientific knowledge and contemporary human experience of a technological society.

I don't think the Church can hope to regain the ability to bring the influence of Christian principles to bear on the formation of opinion and intellectual fashion until the conflict between science and theology has been resolved.

I think two things are needed before such a reconciliation can take place. The theologians have got to go back to first principles and to assess the absolutely essential elements of Christian teaching. Secondly, it will be necessary to establish to what extent and in what way scientific fact and contemporary technological society has influenced popular outlook and attitudes. I think this is important because the Church seems to have lost its capacity for moral leadership and I believe it is vital that it should regain it.

Apart from losing sight of first principles, I suspect that when things get difficult the tendency is to deal with the simpler problems – leaving the more complex and intractable in the

[45]

'pending' tray. I suspect it is easier to fill the day with the 'mechanical' pastoral duties and ordinary administrative chores than to think out the application of Christian principles to the baffling problems of modern society.

Paradoxically, I suspect that first principles are seen to be so self-evident that all the other duties and responsibilities appear to be more complicated and therefore require more attention.

I shall be sending you a letter I received today from a chap who attended the last Commonwealth Study Conference. The point is that he learnt a general principle at the conference and then found that it could be successfully applied to his particular circumstance. I think it is this general guidance that people need but such guidance must be convincing within contemporary experience and it must be given with confidence and conviction.

PHILIP

Sir,

In one way I was sorry that the final item on the Agenda – The Future of the Church – was left with insufficient time, but in another way it is no bad thing to end a meeting with people still wanting to continue the discussion. And in any case that sort of discussion could have profitably gone on for several complete St George's House consultations!

The basic issue seems to be 'Why has the Church lost credibility?' I completely agree with you that the separation between science and theology has been critical. I also suspect that the difficulty that any institution has in adapting to change is also a major factor. By the time the institution has got over the shock of some radical change, and has thought out the implication of that change for its beliefs, so much time has passed that its beliefs appear to be discredited. And change has been so rapid that interest has moved on to some other aspect. The argument over evolution is a typical example of this process. Thirdly, the very process of change places the institution into a permanently defensive position, so that it is always responding and seldom initiating. Any institution in this position has in itself the seeds of its own demise. But I would guess that this is a problem that faces all institutions and not only the Church.

MICHAEL MANN

Dear Michael,
  I was given the enclosed work recently [*Archetype*, by Anthony Stevens] and I found a lot of it very interesting. You may be amused to see that one of the chapters is headed 'A Question of Balance'!

PHILIP

Sir,
  Thank you for sending me *Archetype*. I am intrigued at the way those brought up within scientific disciplines are finding that the so-called antithesis between science and religion may be a mirage. And that both science and religion may have different ways of saying the same thing. This strengthens my conviction that Truth must be followed wherever she leads. And if one is faithful in that quest, although apparent contradictions may appear at first, these very contradictions will, in due course, be resolved by further knowledge and will lead the Christian to a deeper knowledge of God. And that, I suppose, is partly what I mean when I speak of faith: the ability to hold on to ultimate spiritual 'truths' even though they cannot be proved rationally in the 'faith' that eventually intuition and feeling may be seen to have a validity of their own, and to provide their own contribution of proof, when balanced with rational evidence.

The author's ability to harmonize this balance between nature and spirit, reason and emotion, thinking and feeling, is very helpful. I particularly like his description of Marxism as 'the greatest secular myth of our time'.

I think, incidentally, that you might be interested in the enclosed article by Charles Birch.

MICHAEL MANN

[Enclosure]

DID DARWIN GET IT WRONG?

CHARLES BIRCH

The Darwinian theory of evolution is a kingpin of biology. 'Nothing in biology makes sense except in the light of the theory of evolution' said Theodosius Dobzhansky. And most biologists agree. Moreover, this theory has influenced man's image of himself and his place in nature more than any other theory in biology. It has even been invoked to support Marxism, capitalism, racism, fascism and atheism. And just when it seemed to be most secure with the triumph of Neo-Darwinism, which combines Darwin's ideas with modern genetics and palaeontology, we find it under attack from a number of quarters, on radio and television and in magazines and books under titles such as 'Darwin on Trial', 'Why Darwin Got It Wrong', 'Evolution Theory Challenged' and most recently the book by Rattray Taylor (1983) 'The Great Evolution Mystery'. In 1981 the President of the Royal Society, SirAndrew Huxley, saw fit to centre his presidential address to the annual meeting of the society on some of these challenges to Darwinism (Huxley, 1982). He referred, amongst other things, to an address of Sir Edmund Leach given to the 1981 meeting of the British Association on the progress of anthropology in the last 150 years. In this address Leach said 'Many well qualified scientists of the highest standing would today accept many of Wilberforce's criticisms of Darwin.' The reference is of course to Bishop Wilberforce who was confronted by T. H. Huxley at a meeting of the British Association in Oxford in 1860. Huxley's great grandson now finds himself answering the challenge of a latter day champion of Wilberforce!

Why this renewed criticism of Darwinism and what is the relevance of the modern debate to the Christian understanding of the creation? Before pursuing these questions it is well to remember that Darwinian evolution has been under attack ever since its birth in 1859. Contrary to common belief, the first opponents of it were not churchmen but Darwin's scientific colleagues. The debates that started in the autumn of 1859 saw few scientists supporting Darwin. They felt that the scientific basis for evolution by natural selection was wholly inadequate. It is usually assumed that *The Origin of Species* provided a strong factual basis for Darwin's theory of the mechanism of evolution. It did not. Darwin's argument can be broken down into four elements. First, the rate of reproduction of all species is far greater than the carrying capacity of their environment, hence the 'struggle for existence'. Second, there is much variation between the individuals of the species. Third, some individuals are better adapted to survive and reproduce than others in the struggle, i.e. they vary in 'fitness' hence 'natural selection'. Fourth, the favourable characteristics of the survivors are inherited and in the course of time this will transform the species. In 1859 there was no doubt that the first two elements of the argument were correct. The remaining two were not solidly based on observation and experiment. They were conjectures or reasonable hypotheses.

The Origin provided a lot of evidence for the theory that animals and plants had evolved. But Darwin recognized that this would carry little weight until he had worked out a credible theory as to how they had evolved. That is why he waited for 25 years before publishing the theory. In the event, what convinced Darwin did not convince his fellow biologists for a decade or more. The main arguments brought against Darwin during this time are ably marshalled by Moore (1979). *The Origin* did provide a stimulus for studies on comparative anatomy and palaeontology and it was these studies which gradually persuaded scientists that evolution had happened. Yet it was not until after 1930 that biologists became persuaded about the Darwinian mechanism of evolution by natural selection. From 1930 onwards mathematical models, observation and experiment provided a lot of evidence in support of natural selection of genetical variation within the species, evidence which even the creationists now accept. What the latter do not accept is that these processes can result in the transformation of one species into another. They claim that no one has witnessed such an event so it does not happen. This comes rather oddly from people who claim that Adam and Eve were created *de novo* in the Garden of Eden. But it is not true to say that no one has witnessed the transformation of one species into another. Dobzhansky (1953) felt obliged to point this out to Pope Pius XII after the Pope had made some such remark to geneticists in Rome. Dobzhansky pointed out that the plant *Raphanobrassica* is a new species created from two other genera *Raphanus* and *Brassica*. It is not only distinct in appearance but is unable to cross with its parental species and is yet quite fertile with itself. It is one of many such examples among plants.

In 1927 J. B. S. Haldane wrote an essay entitled 'Darwinism Today'. It was headed with a quotation from Hilaire Belloc 'Darwinism is dead'. He then proceeded to show that Darwinism was very much alive. In 1982 the English evolutionary biologist John Maynard Smith wrote an essay on 'Evolution after Darwin' in the *London Review of Books* which concluded thus: 'Those who would like to believe that Darwin is dead, whether because they are creationists, or because they dislike the apparently Thatcherite conclusions which have been drawn from his theory, or find the mathematics of population genetics too hard for them, would be well advised to be cautious lest the reports of his death have been exaggerated.'

There are three streams in the current debate about Darwinism. One comes from mathematicians and physicists, a second comes from within biology and a third comes from religious creationists.

The Arguments of Mathematics about Chance

A conference was held 15 years ago in Princeton at the behest of mathematicians on 'Mathematical challenges to the Neo-Darwinian theory of evolution'. The gist of the criticism is the old one about the monkeys and typewriters, that a thousand monkeys hitting away at random at a thousand typewriters for a thousand or more years would not produce the works of Shakespeare. We all agree. A more modern version comes from Sir Fred Hoyle and Chandra Wick-ramasinghe (1981) who put the chance of a chance origin of living

[50]

matter as one in ten to the power 40,000 which is to say impossible. This is an estimate of the chance that 2,000 enzyme molecules will be formed simultaneously from their component amino acids on a single specified occasion – the equivalent says Wickramasinghe of a tornado blowing through a junk yard and producing a jumbo jet. This sort of argument is very quickly dismissed by biologists as it bears no resemblance to any understanding they have of the evolution of life. It ignores the step by step process of Darwinian evolution. What is impossible in one step can be achieved in a succession of steps. The bacterium *Escherichia coli* that contains five mutant genes for resistance to the antibiotic penicillin is resistant to a very high concentration of penicillin. Now the chance that a single mutation will occur is one in 10^8. The chance that five different mutations will occur simultaneously is one in 10^{40} which is the same as saying it is impossible. Yet by a step by step process we can get five mutant genes in one bacterium. It happens this way. If a hundred million non-resistant bacteria are put in a medium containing a very low concentration of penicillin less than ten will survive. These ten each contain a single similar gene for resistance. These resistant survivors can now be multiplied and millions put in still higher concentrations of penicillin. Again only a few survive. These are those bacteria which have undergone a second mutation and so each has two genes for resistance. Repeat the process in yet a higher concentration of penicillin and after five successive steps we have bacteria that contain five mutant genes. What is impossible in one step can be achieved in successive steps of mutation, reproduction and selection. The same argument applies to the evolution in complex organs such as the human eye. The relevant question for Hoyle and Wickramasinghe to ask is the chance of some far simpler combination of molecules than 2,000 enzymes being formed at any place on earth within a billion years. But it would be absurd to approach even that simpler question on the supposition that complex molecules are a consequence of random coming together of atoms. They are not. There are rules of assembly of atoms and molecules. They are not like inert billiard balls bounding around at random in the universe. They are more like men and women in an old time dance in which firstly each individual gets a partner then the partners form into larger organized groupings until perhaps all the dancers are dancing as one. The more I learn about atoms and molecules the more they look like living entities that have their 'likes' and 'dislikes' if you will. Indeed it is the conviction of some of us that life could not have originated and evolved if the 'building blocks' were the sort of objects that mathematicians juggle with. Atoms and molecules are 'subjects' that respond to their environment and are changed with changing relationships to their environment. When you start with the classical notion of atoms as self-contained machines and propose that atoms in brains are the same as atoms not in brains and when you then try to build up a living organism from such atoms you produce a machine. That is the mechanistic model of life which has to be challenged. Alfred North Whitehead (1926, p. 157) pointed this out when he wrote:

'A thoroughgoing evolutionary philosophy is inconsistent with materialism. The aboriginal stuff or material from which a materialistic philosophy starts is incapable of evolution. This material is in itself the ultimate substance. Evolution, on the materialistic theory, is reduced to the role of being another word for the description of the changes of the external relations between portions of matter. There is nothing to evolve, because one set of external relations is as good as any other set of external relations. There can merely be change. purposeless and unprogressive. . . . The doctrine thus cries aloud for a conception of organism as fundamental for nature.'

What Whitehead called the conception of organism Birch and Cobb (1981) called the ecological model of nature. Our book is an attempt to expound this idea as a challenge to mechanism.

The Challenge from within Biology

A second stream in the debate about Darwinism comes from within biology. It is really a debate within the Darwinian framework although the challengers sometimes claim otherwise. Gould and Eldredge (1977) who are both palaeontologists put forward the view that evolution is not a gradual process but consists of long periods of stasis followed by 'geologically instant' change. They call this 'punctuated equilibrium'. Much to their annoyance creationists claim this as evidence for creationism, which of course it is not. The view seems to run counter to the conclusions of the great palaeontologist G. G. Simpson who wrote *Tempo and Mode in Evolution*

(Simpson, 1944) to demonstrate that the major changes as well as the micro-changes in evolution are best understood as a succession of gradual changes. It is also well to remember that Simpson said evolution 'leaps' as well as 'creeps'. A critical problem in this debate is that palaeontologists deal in a completely different time-scale to geneticists. A million years to a geneticist are but a day to the palaeontologist. This point is very clearly made in a splendid article on the subject written for everyman by Rensberger (1982) which goes somewhat as follows. Under strong natural selection a new species could probably evolve in 50 to 100 generations according to geneticists. By contrast Gould and Eldredge allowed that as much as 100,000 or more years could be considered a brief period of speciation. Even in a long-lived species this is enough for 5,000 generations. A species that took 100,000 years to evolve would be considered by palaeontologists to have appeared almost instantly. The layers of rocks that preserve fossils are formed in such an irregular manner that 100,000 or sometimes even a million years can fail to be preserved. On the other hand, geneticists who work with fruit flies that turn over many generations in a year and produce new varieties with ease would consider any change taking 100,000 years as excruciatingly gradual. Gould and Eldredge consider 100,000 years is an instant compared with several million years of stasis that may ensue. Furthermore, what appears to the palaeontologist as stasis may be anything but that for the organism (since the palaeontologist only looks at hard parts). John Maynard Smith to whom I have already referred considers that punctuationist views will prove to be a ripple rather than a revolution in the history of ideas about evolution. His view is well argued also by geneticists Stebbins and Ayala (1981). A more important controversy within biology concerns the extent to which genetical changes that occur in evolution are adaptive or neutral. It seems, contrary to earlier views, that genes can accumulate in the organism that may have little adaptive significance. The issue is the extent to which this happens. This is still a matter of experimentation and discussion. It is an example of how the details of Neo-Darwinism change every year.

The Creationists

A third stream in the debate comes from the creationists and more especially from the Institute for Creation Research in San Diego and the Creation Research Society. Evolutionary theory and particularly Darwinism are charged with being a root cause of the disintegration of valued institutions: the family, morality, religion, even science itself. This is the stated reason for the creationists' campaign against evolution. It features strongly in the propaganda of the Moral Majority in the US against evolution. However, the real reason is that evolutionary theory runs counter to a literal reading of the first two chapters of Genesis. Creationists are out to try and demonstrate that evidence biologists use to support the theory that living organisms have evolved is not evidence at all. A well known example is the booklet by Duane Gish *Evolution: The Fossils Say No*. It is extremely difficult if not impossible for people who are not palaeontologists to make any judgment at all on what the fossils say. An implication of the theory of evolution is that there must have been transition forms between species and other groups of organisms. In Darwin's day there was almost no direct evidence of this at all. Since then many gaps have been filled. There are, for example, good transition fossils linking the classes of vertebrates: fish, amphibia, birds and mammals. Gish denies that there are any transition forms. For example *Archaeopteryx* is regarded as a transition between reptiles and birds. Gish says it is a bird. Unless one knows the details of skeletons of birds and reptiles it is impossible to know who is correct. The exercise in this particular case has been done for the general reader by Ruse (1982) in his excellent book *Darwinism Defended* (p. 312); *Archaeopteryx* is a transition form between reptiles and birds. In Darwin's time there were few known transition forms. Today there are many. Yet there are also many gaps. Indeed, it is practically the rule that transition forms between the orders of animals (Primates and Marsupials are orders of mammals) are unknown. But this does not imply that transition forms never existed. A full discussion of this problem can be found in Simpson (1953).

Until recently biologists felt they had better things to do than answer the creationists. That has now changed. A flood of books has begun to appear on the subject of which the first are Kitcher (1982) and Newell (1982). The reason for the change is the increasing number of supporters for creationism in the US (probably more than half the adult population), and more especially their efforts to have legislation changed in some two dozen American states enabling creationism to be given equal time with evolution in biology courses in high schools. John A. Moore (1975) is, to my knowledge, the only evolutionist who has pursued the problem of what equal time for creation and evolution would involve. He carefully analyses the problems raised by interpreting Genesis literally and concludes that if the creationists were rigorous about this they would destroy their own case.

In the early phases of the debate creationists argued that creationism was a science; they called it creation science. However, since a Federal judge ruled that creationism was not a science (*Time*, 18 January 1982, p. 31) they have changed their tune. Now they argue that neither creation nor evolution are science. They are philosophies or religions. The issues here are quite complex for they raise the question – what is science? There are lots of views about that. Without pursuing that question here I can happily refer to a fine discussion of the issue in the context of creationism by Kitcher (1982) in *The Abuse of Science: The Case against Creationism*. This is a scholarly book that contains an excellent discussion of the distinction between science and pseudo-science. A history of the American controversy is given in Ruse (1982), Newell (1982), Numbers (1982) and Kitcher (1982). The journal *Creation/Evolution* (P.O. Box 146, Amherst Branch, Buffalo, NY 14226) provides useful material for teachers and others on the evolutionist answers to specific issues raised by creationists. For those interested in pursuing a non-literal interpretation of Genesis the following are helpful guides: Baker (1979), Koch (1979), Richardson (1959) and Westerman (1974).

The creationist campaign is not simply a campaign against evolutionary biology. It concentrates an attack on the whole of science. In order to accommodate science to creationism the creationists have to change the meaning of the 2nd law of thermo-dynamics, the constancy of speed of light, the established means of ageing the earth and its rocks and as well the meaning of what is a science. This is what 'creation research' is all about. It would imply a rewriting of textbooks in science. Indeed they already do this in biology. The campaign has also influenced the content of non-creationist biology tests. Many publishers now soft-peddle evolution for fear that their books will not be sold in the southern states of the US. The influence in education has been bad. Yet there is one small redeeming feature. Evolution has been and still is taught dogmatically in many institutions. One textbook I recall starts with the sentence

[55]

'All life has descended by transformation from one original form of life'. This is a hypothesis for which there is considerable evidence. It is not an irrefutable fact. Students are easily misled by such statements. We can state the facts and then indicate that evolution is a framework within which these facts comfortably fit at least for the time being. The same approach can be and should be made to the theory of the electron, to relativity and all other broad-scale theories in science.

The Real Challenge to Science and to the Churches

Darwinism, despite the title of Darwin's great work, is not primarily about the origin of species. It is about the origin of the adaptive diversity of life. That is the central question of biology. How is it that plants and animals are so beautifully adapted, some to live in the depths of the oceans, others on the tops of high mountains, some in hot springs, others in frozen seas? How is it that an orchid that grows not far from where I am writing has flowers that for all the world look like a wasp that lives in the same region? When the orchid flowers in January the male wasp emerges from its pupal case in the soil and goes in search of a female wasp. But there are none to be found as they emerge later. What it does find is the orchid whose flower looks like a female wasp. Indeed the flower is such a good mimic of the wasp that the male wasp mates with the orchid carrying the process to consummation. At the same time it pollinates the orchid with pollen from another flower. Not only does the flower look like a wasp it also gives off an odour which attracts the male wasp. Such adaptations of plants and animals have puzzled man from time immemorial. Darwin's theory is an attempt to provide a scientific explanation of them and as such has been highly successful.

However the way Darwinism is taught is another matter. More often than not it is presented as a completely mechanical procedure in which chance and chance alone is the predominant feature. All that such a procedure could produce is machines, if even that. An extreme statement of this sort of presentation is made by Monod (1972, pp. 137 and 167).

'Our number came up in the Monte Carlo game . . . man at last knows he is alone in the unfeeling immensity of the universe, out of which he emerged only by chance.'

Because chance plays a role in evolution and in life is no reason for

[56]

supposing that it has the only or even predominant role. There is chance and there is purpose. Indeed purpose and choice of the evolving creature play a role in its own evolution. The creature creates its own environment. And at a deeper level, if we are willing to grant that living organisms and indeed their constituent molecules are subjects as well as objects, then purpose has a major role to play in evolution and in livingness itself (see Birch and Cobb, 1982). But science has failed to make this clear. It has failed to bestow values on the facts with which it deals. It too readily reduces the universe and the human to contrivance or machine. Yet we know ourselves to be sensitive, feeling, responsive creatures. Darwinism explains much. But the full development of the aesthetic and moral sense and the capacity for abstract thought still elude its grasp. The Einsteins, the Leonardo da Vincis and the Suffering Servant do not fit easily into the scheme. Nor does Darwinism together with classical physics and chemistry account for the evolution of consciousness. On the basis of classical physics and mechanistic biology all that need evolve are mechanical robots without consciousness. The existence of consciousness in ourselves raises questions that a mechanistic physics and a mechanistic biology cannot answer. They cry aloud for another model which will yet be faithful to the facts of science.

Because science fails to bestow values on the facts with which it deals it has contributed to a worldwide malaise, a sense of meaninglessness. Furthermore, it is plain for all to see that scientific rationalism has failed to solve our major problems. In the name of scientific objectivity scientism gives an emasculated vision of the world and all that is in it. The wave of anti-scientism from creationists and various cults and sects is an extreme response to this more widely felt malaise. And as Dorothy Nelkin (1977) points out in her book on the textbook controversy, the loudest advocates of creationism are not from uneducated backgrounds. They tend to be middle-class technically trained citizens. She refers to the 'paradox' that Fundamentalist beliefs tend to flourish in those parts of the US which have recently become centres of industries of high technology such as southern California and Texas. Our technological rationality is letting people down.

It is not enough for science and rationality to expose pseudo-science, false mythology, religious obscurantism and superstition. It has to do more than just clear away rubbish. Somehow we have to show that science deals with subjects, with entities that feel and respond and anticipate and are thereby creative. We have to show that the scientific experience and the aesthetic and religious experience can be integrated into a richer vision of life and its purposes. Science has failed to do this and so have the churches. We live in a schizophrenic world of our own making. It is time for the churches to wake up to the great opportunity this crisis of thought and life presents to them. The alternative is to shut its doors to the world. And science too has to look to its laurels. I agree with Catherine Roberts (1982, p. 180) who wrote ' . . . there is something inherently askew about the present thrust of biology and medicine that needs to be put right. This view rests on the belief that mankind is entering a new age that will demand of the life sciences something quite different from what sciences are now prepared to give. The future contributions of the life sciences will be more holistic and more enabling than any that are being made now.' And 'A truer, more holistic vision of the universe and its different levels of reality requires insight that can relate science to questions of good and evil and final cause. Nor can scientific investigation long survive without a more fully developed conscience.' (Roberts, 1983, p. 8). Both science and religion need liberation. That's a task for science and the churches.

REFERENCES

Baker, John A. 1979. *Anticipation* 25: 40–6.

Birch, Charles, and Cobb, John B. Jr. 1981. *The Liberation of Life: From Cell to Community*. Cambridge University Press.

Dobzhansky, Th. 1953. Comment on the discussion of genetics by His Holiness Pius XII. *Science* 118: 561–63.

Gould, S. J., and Eldredge, N. 1977. Punctuated equilibria: the tempo and mode of evolution reconsidered. *Paleobiology* 3: 115–51.

Hoyle, F., and Wickramasinghe, N. C. 1981. *Evolution from Space*. J. M. Dent, London.

Huxley, Andrew. 1982. Address of the President of the Royal Society, Sir Andrew Huxley, at the anniversary meeting 30 November 1981. Proc. Roy. Soc. Lond. B. 214: 137–52.

Kitcher, Philip. 1982. *Abusing Science: The Case Against Creationism*. MIT Press, Cambridge, Mass.

Koch, Klaus. 1979. The Old Testament view of nature. *Anticipation* 25: 47–52.

Monod, Jacques. 1972. *Chance and Necessity*. Collins, London.

Moore, John A. 1975. On giving equal time to the teaching of evolution and creation. *Perspectives in Biology and Medicine* 18: 405–17.

Moore, John A. 1979. Creationism. In: *Science Education and Society*. Eds. Abraham, M. R., and Fox, F. W. pp. 145–64. Ohio State University.

Nelkin, Dorothy. 1977. *Science Textbook Controversies and the Politics of Equal Time*. MIT Press, Cambridge, Mass.

Newell, Norman D. 1982. *Creation and Evolution: Myth or Reality*. Columbia University Press, New York.

Numbers, Ronald I. 1982. Creationism in 20th-century America. *Science* 218: 538–44.

Rensberger, Boyce. 1982. Evolution since Darwin. *Science* 82: 3: 40–45.

Richardson, Alan. 1959. *Genesis I–XI*. SCM Press, London.

Roberts, Catherine. 1982. Biology and the New Age: an Evolutionary and Ethical Assessment. *Perspectives in Biology and Medicine* 25 (2): 176–93.

Roberts, Catherine. 1983. Insight in Science and in Plato. *Manas* 36 (9): 1–8.

Ruse, Michael. 1982. *Darwinism Defended: A Guide to the Evolution Controversies*. Addison – Wesley, Reading, Mass.

Simpson, George Gaylord. 1944. *Tempo and Mode in Evolution*. Columbia University Press, New York.

Simpson, George Gaylord. 1953. *The Major Features of Evolution*. Columbia University Press, New York.

Stebbins, G. Ledyard, and Ayala, Francisco J. 1981. Is a New Evolutionary Synthesis Necessary? *Science* 213: 967–71.

Taylor, Gordon Rattray. 1983. *The Great Evolution Mystery*. Secker, London.

Westerman, Claus. 1974. *Creation*. SPCK, London.

Whitehead, A. N. 1926. *Science and the Modern World*. Macmillan, New York.

Dear Michael,

Thank you for the cutting about evolution. As you say, it covers the issues very well. I was particularly interested to read the last part because, as you know, the relationship between scientists and theologians has been one of my hobby-horses. I was glad to find someone else even faintly interested!

One thing about Darwin is that he explains in great detail the basis of his theory, whereas the Creationists merely state their convictions without any substantiation beyond divine enlightenment. Incidentally, how do the Creationists account for the disappearance of species such as the dinosaurs? Was it an act of God – if so why? Or was it down to a 'chance' change in the climate?

The trouble with creating anything is that the creator has little, if any, further influence on its performance. The maker of a roulette wheel cannot specify which slots the ball will fall into. The motor car manufacturer cannot decide the ultimate fate of his productions. So it could be agreed that once God had created the universe and decided upon its general layout the precise sequence of subsequent events depended on the interaction of its components and the characteristics He gave to them. In other words it may be chance that decides which slot the ball falls into at each turn of the roulette wheel but then the roulette wheel was deliberately created so that this 'chance' effect could take place. There is no 'chance' factor in the creation of the roulette wheel.

Could it be that what looks like chance to us in the evolutionary system was deliberately planned into it in the first place?

PHILIP

Sir,

I am afraid that I cannot take the Creationists' argument too seriously. For me it smacks too much of the early defensiveness

[60]

of the nineteenth-century Church against what appeared to be a shaking of their foundations. What really seems to trouble the Creationists is the deterioration of certain social institutions which they value highly; the family, morality, the Church, etc. In this I share their concern. But where I part company with them is in the way in which they look for a scapegoat to blame, for in challenging the Bible as literal truth and choosing Darwinism they then construct a counter- argument based on a literal interpretation of the Old Testament. It seems to me that, instead of taking the results of research and new knowledge and saying 'How does this affect our understanding of God?', they have constructed a theory and then looked for evidence to bolster their predetermined views. Surely the essence of the search for truth must be an open mind and a willingness to examine old theories when new knowledge seems to challenge their validity? Secondly, I believe that the Creationist approach only succeeds in achieving the opposite of what it sets out to do. It is basically authoritarian; it sets out to accommodate science to itself by attacking it and by arbitrarily changing its rules. The danger lies that – in rejecting the Creationists and all that they stand for – the institutions which the Creationists seek to defend also become rejected, because they become identified with this method of defence and so are discredited along with it. If Windsor Castle is taken over by terrorists and defended against attack, the terrorists may be dealt with, but so often it is the Castle which suffers the damage.

The point you make about Darwin explaining his theory in great detail as against the bland and barely substantiated statements of the Creationists exposes this typical authoritarian stance. The appeal of authoritarianism lies in its dogmatic conviction, especially to frightened and confused people. It gives them reassurance in areas where they do not seek to question too deeply, but it is the antithesis of any search for truth.

The issue of 'chance' which you raise is a much more difficult one for the theologian, and its probable explanation is, in my

[61]

view, more likely to depend upon a question of balance. I believe in a Creator – God. If God is loving and caring, He presumably cares for what happens to His universe, and indeed the Christian goes so far to say that 'God so loved the world, that He gave His only son, Jesus Christ, that the world might be saved'. Some of the Fundamentalists would then go on to say that all our actions are part of a predetermined plan, and that whatever we do we are – in that sense – fulfilling God's purpose. This seems to me to reduce us to automatons and to deny the reality of free will. I believe that God so loved His creation that, in the case of man, He created him in His own image, especially in the sense that He gave man free will. God acted deliberately because true love can only be true if it is freely and willingly given. Love cannot be compelled. If we are to love God or our neighbour, we can only do so truly if it is our own free conscious wish and decision. But with this gift of free will comes the appalling risk that we fail to respond, and we have the power to reject God and His love for us, and to be cruel and unkind to our neighbour. In this sense God's dilemma is that if He wants the highest for us, He has to give us free will, and if He gives us free will, He has to accept the risk of rejection.

This is the theme of the Old Testament. Follow God and obey His laws, and all will be well. Ignore God and disobey His laws, and you get yourself into a mess. The New Testament takes this a stage further in placing before us a higher ethic of 'love', and also setting our finite worldly existence into the context not only of the past and present but also the future, and takes that future beyond this life.

This is, of course, a gross over-simplification. It is not just a matter of either predestination or free will. Freedom and purpose are intertwined. The behavioural sciences have shown us how we are influenced by heredity and environment, and are not as free as we might be led to believe.

If I have argued so far purely in terms of *homo sapiens*, I do not see why the basis of such an argument cannot be applied to all forms of life. The real question seems to lie in the origin of the adaptive diversity of life. Surely it cannot be due to pure mathematical chance? From a biological point of view is change due to adaptive reasons, or is it just neutral? Surely the answer must lie somewhere in a statement of balance, that change and evolution are both by chance and by purpose. The weakness of Darwinism is that it fails to tackle the aesthetic and moral issues, and these depend upon consciousness. Classical physics and mechanistic biology would reduce us to' the status of automatons. And it is against the facts of science. We need an explanation that will deal not only with mechanical answers, but one which takes a whole view of life in all its complexity and immensity. It will have to give life a meaning and a sense of value, for if it does not, it is not faithful to the facts as we know them, and therefore, in that sense, fails to be scientific. Science is geared to answer the 'how' questions, whilst religion is being challenged to answer the 'why' questions.

Whether or not religion can respond to this challenge is the real issue for Christians. Until recently man has been satisfied with a simplistic view of God. Darwin has challenged that simplicity, but has not, in my view, provided a satisfactory answer. We are being called to a much deeper and more profound understanding of God at work in His universe. The challenge to Darwin by the mathematicians and by the physicists and biologists comes from within science itself. The religious dimension is to relate all this to conscience, values and questions of good and evil, and final purpose. I find this a very exciting prospect. The religious contribution will not be successfully made by backwoods conservatism, but by an open mind willing to consider and balance the relative merits of all aspects of the debate.

MICHAEL MANN

Evolution and Morality

Evolution and Morality

Dear Michael,

You make a very good point about the Creationists bringing into disrepute the very institutions they seek to defend. This is not an isolated case. Opposition to birth control is another example.

I would like to take you up on the issue of 'chance'. As I understand it, theologians don't like the idea of evolution because they consider that it is purely a result of chance. But that is a subjective view. The way in which species have developed may appear to them to be by chance, but why do they deny the possibility that circumstances giving rise to genetic changes were not part of God's design? They are apparently quite content with the instant creation of species but not with a system that achieves the same end over a longer period of time. Even theologians must realize that not all members of the same species are identical in every respect. People vary very greatly in their physical as well as in their mental construction. Do they deny that this variation is due to chance? If they do it means that they believe that God was responsible for the variation, in which case He is presumably also responsible for the natural consequences of such variation.

If they don't deny it – in other words, if they accept that it is due to chance – then why do they find it so difficult to accept that the consequences are due to the same chance?

Incidentally, you imply yourself that God is prepared to put things to chance by His gift of free will. As you say, He has to accept the 'risk of rejection' which is the same as saying that rejection is a matter of chance.

You go on to imply that the 'adaptive diversity of life cannot be due to pure mathematical chance'. No evolutionist has ever claimed any such thing. The chances are definitely not mathematical, indeed the adaptive improvement of species depends very much on the genetic diversity of the population, the environmental pressures on it, and on the 'will' of the species to survive. As you know, there are many cases of species under pressure simply giving up the struggle by failing to produce any young or sufficient young to maintain the population. Some species, even of the same genus, are more vigorous and numerically successful than others. Look at the grey and red squirrel.

I think you are a little unfair on Darwin when you say he has not supplied a satisfactory answer. I would say that he has provided a reasonable explanation of how the system works; it is the theologians who have steadfastly refused to consider the implications and failed to develop a 'deeper and more profound understanding of God at work in His Universe' with the knowledge put at their disposal by Darwin.

To me, at any rate, the concept of instant creation is not tenable, for a number of practical reasons, and also because it is too simplistic. Equally, I am not convinced by the mathematical and statistical arguments against Darwin. It is precisely such arguments that reduce the whole thing to some mechanistic inflexible system whereas the whole beauty of the idea of natural selection is that it is part and parcel of God's gift of free will.

I also find great attraction to evolution from the moral point of view. Natural selection ensures success through improved adaptation. It is true that not all mankind behaves in a very satisfactory way (free will again) but as a piece of evolutionary adaptive improvement from single-cell organisms it is quite an achievement. Furthermore, the adaptive process is also at work on man's behaviour. 'Those who live by the sword, die by the sword', while the most prosperous and civilized communities have lived in peace and justice usually inspired by a high moral and religious philosophy. The whole system

[68]

encourages improvement, and although it is not proof against 'accidents', it normally requires a positively evil action to bring about a deterioration.

PHILIP

Sir,

Your letter raises a whole series of points which I cannot let go unchallenged! You say that theologians do not like the idea of evolution because it seems to them to be purely a result of chance. I just do not think that that statement is true. There may be some theologians at either end of the theological spectrum who might think that. But I would judge that the solid core of reputable theological thought is basically agnostic about evolution. As I have said in earlier letters, Darwin merely pushes the argument about God one stage further back, but it still leaves unanswered the possibility of an eventual transcendent conscious being.

The Neo-Darwinians claim to be able to explain evolution in terms of random mutation, Mendelian genetics and natural selection. This is essentially a mechanistic framework of thought which seeks to explain the phenomena of life in terms of physics and chemistry. And surely it is the Neo-Darwinians who have tended to become mechanistic, rather than those who attack Darwin? But it still does not account for the origin of species, and it runs into serious difficulties with the psychologists over problems concerning the interaction of the mind with the body. In addition, botanists and biologists are now raising questions about morphogenesis, and physicists are raising questions about relativity and quantum theory, for which Darwinism is not able to provide an answer. Indeed they point out that when so little is known, for example, about morphogenesis and behaviour, and since living organisms cannot yet be fully explained in terms of the known laws of physics and chemistry, it is, at the very least, an open question that these could depend upon factors as yet unrecognized by

[69]

physics. Furthermore these biologists and physicists and psychologists would say Darwinism is no longer being used as a rigorously definable scientific theory, but that it is made to justify a conservative method of working within an established framework provided by existing physics and chemistry.

So I think that many theologians are almost sitting in the grandstand watching the scientists argue it out. This is not to say that they are not interested or not involved. But the argument within science itself is so complex and requires such specialized scientific knowledge that they do not feel competent to intervene at this stage. If, as some scientists are now saying (botanists like Sheldrake, physicists like Bohm, or of course Jung and Stevens on behalf of psychology), that there may be a metaphysical explanation and dimension, then the theologians may be able to contribute. But metaphysics can hardly make a contribution when Darwinians deny its existence.

So I think that you are being unfair in saying that the theologians have failed to use the knowledge put at their disposal by Darwin. I believe that many theologians accept a lot of what Darwin has suggested, but they still are doubtful about what has become, in Darwinism, a mechanistic approach. And here it is important to distinguish between what Darwin himself wrote, and the way in which the Neo-Darwinians have developed these theories. But I must also not be too defensive on behalf of theologians, because I am extremely critical of the way in which theology has failed us.

What I find immensely exciting is the way in which many scientists who started out as atheists or agnostics are, as a result of their research, coming up with paper after paper which suggest that God and metaphysics may, after all, be needed to solve some problems which baffle scientists using more traditional scientific methods. And this questioning is coming from within science itself, and from a wide range of scientific disciplines: physics, botany, biology, astronomy, psychology – to name but a few.

As to the particular issue of 'chance', you may or may not be right. I see and appreciate the attraction which it has for you. I remain agnostic until the arguments have been carried further. Again I tend to agree with you over instant creation, although the Big Bang theory is held by many as a possible explanation. But even if 'mankind's evolutionary adaptive improvement from single cell organisms is quite an achievement', and is proved to be true, the question still remains – 'How did the single cell originate?'

One final point: I really cannot agree that even if 'the most prosperous and civilized communities have lived in peace and justice usually inspired by a high moral and religious philosophy', that 'the whole system encourages improvement'. In the first place, I doubt whether history would substantiate the first statement, and the second is against all the evidence. Civilizations grow, rise and fall, and the fall is invariably due to the internal weakness and corruption brought about by the enjoyment of previous success. It seems that prosperity and civilization also have within them the seeds of dissolution due to human greed, laziness, and selfishness, followed by a weakening of justice and a decay of religion and morality, and the collapse of that civilization. Where has any system in history encouraged improvement?

I do not think any theory will be truly satisfactory until it takes into account the *whole* of existence. Darwin has made a great contribution, but he ignores certain aspects of our experience, and his theory cannot satisfactorily explain other aspects of new knowledge. What is needed more than anything is to relate man's metaphysical side to his physical aspect. And it is scientists who are trying to do this.

In my view, it is at this point that the theologians need to enter the argument, for they are meant to be the metaphysical specialists, and it is here that their contribution is needed. At present this theological field is only considered and taught at a very few universities, and that is a pretty bad record.

MICHAEL MANN

[71]

Dear Michael,

There are a few points in your letter which have provoked me into further comment.

You suggest that 'Darwin merely pushes the argument about God one stage further back'. I would not agree. Perhaps it moves the argument about the origin of life further back, but surely that is not God's sole point or purpose? You also say that scientists are coming to believe that 'God and metaphysics may be needed, etc.' Again, surely God does not exist merely so as to explain the inexplicable? It is true that the Old Testament uses Him to explain everything that was not understood and as so little was understood He was used to explain a great deal more than He is today. But that it is not the God of the New Testament.

I have to admit that I am not well informed about Neo-Darwinians or exactly what they believe, but in my opinion they are being naive to imagine that evolution is merely a matter of 'random mutation, Mendelian genetics and natural selection'. Those are all factors but they are not the only factors.

I am quite sure that the scientists find difficulty with many of the facts of life and behaviour, particularly if they try to reduce everything to conform to the laws of physics and chemistry as they are accepted to be at the moment. In fact I am rather tempted to say that the argument within science is very similar to the discussion about angels on the head of a pin. Anyway why should Darwinians deny the existence of metaphysics? After all, religion itself is a factor in that process considering that Roman Catholic and Buddhist priests and nuns have to remain celibate!

However I believe the crux of our discussion centres on your 'final point'. I still maintain that prosperous and civilized communities do live in peace and justice and that this is achieved because they are inspired by a moral and religious philosophy and I believe history does substantiate that statement. Of course civilizations fail because of all the factors you mention, but those factors only explain the failure of what had been a success.

You ask 'Where has any system in history encouraged improvement?' My point was that it is the process of evolution that encourages improvement – unless of course you maintain that a single cell organism is 'better' than *homo sapiens* as a physical being. The process – not the system – of evolution also works for improvement in other ways as it discourages 'failure' and encourages 'success'. For example, the process by which scientists seek to arrive at the truth is an evolutionary process. Unsatisfactory theories are rejected while those that appear to satisfy all the factors are adopted. In engineering the same applies; the best solutions are repeated, unsatisfactory solutions are rejected. In manufacturing the companies which get all the factors more right than their competitors are 'selected', the others go bankrupt. Much the same could be said about religions. Naturally 'failure' and 'success' are relatively subjective terms but history does show that 'wrong' policies end in 'failure' and that failure is usually in the form of economic or social collapse, revolution or military defeat. The problem, of course, is that man never seems to be able to learn from previous mistakes. Each generation seems to have to start from scratch and fall into all the traps and mistakes of its predecessors.

In Darwinian terms it might be argued that Marxism is a 'mutation' as it is not part of evolutionary political systems, it is a complete break with all previous experience. It remains to be seen whether it is selected as an improvement over previously accepted systems, although I find it difficult to believe that any system which sets governors and governed so bitterly against each other could possibly be accepted as an improvement over the, admittedly, not entirely successful conventional systems.

You suggest that no theory is satisfactory unless it 'takes into account the whole of existence'. I don't believe that any single theory can be all-inclusive. Einstein provided a theory

[73]

about mass and energy which still applies to all the physical material world – as far as I know – but it does not set out, as Darwin did, to explain the way in which living species have come to be the way they are. Although Darwin did not enlarge on this theory of natural selection, it seems to me at least that the process of evolution is capable of explaining how the physical laws are applied in practice by suggesting the way scientific, political, technological and, to a certain extent, religious ideas have come to be the way they are at this moment. However it certainly does nothing – and makes no attempt – to explain the physical and chemical phenomena encompassed by Einstein's formula.

PHILIP

Sir,

You are quite right to say that 'God does not exist merely so as to explain the inexplicable'. The point I was trying to make is that some things which, up to now, have been difficult to understand from a purely scientific point of view seem to make much more sense when the scientific analysis is complemented by metaphysical insights. Secondly, some things which were thought to have been established by scientific analysis have been brought into doubt by further scientific research and new knowledge. These doubts are apparently more easily explainable when metaphysical insights are applied. So in the sense I was trying to suggest, some scientists are now seeing theology as a means of shedding light where previously there was a murky darkness.

But you are quite right to say that God must not be used as a 'God of the gaps', just in order to explain what we cannot at present understand. I was attempting to put forward the opposite approach – that some of the things we are struggling to understand seem to point to the possibility of a transcendent being (call that 'being' what you may). And it is now scientists, starting out from an agnostic attitude, who are by their research suggesting this.

On my 'final point', I think that we may be arguing at cross-purposes. I would certainly agree that no civilization can be both prosperous and civilized unless it is supported and inspired by a high moral code and a strong religious belief. And it is the drop in moral standards, and loss of belief, that brings about decline and fall.

I would accept that evolution can encourage improvement, but can it not also improve man's ability to be evil? Jung has written: 'It is not that present-day man is capable of greater evil than the man of antiquity. He merely has more effective means with which to realize his proclivity. As his consciousness and knowledge has broadened, so his moral nature has lagged behind. That is our problem today. Reason alone does not suffice. In the sense that I believe you are using the term 'evolution', surely it is neither good nor bad for humanity; what matters is the use we make of our knowledge and skills. And, as you so rightly say, we never seem to learn from our past mistakes, and therefore 'improvement' tends to be material rather than moral. We do not seem to have the moral ability to combat the cold-blooded cruelty of Auschwitz, or the Gulag Archipelago, nerve gasses or biological warfare.

I would certainly accept that 'no single theory can be all inclusive', but surely every theory must be capable of standing up to insights disclosed by other disciplines? As I understand it, some of the theories put forward by Darwin are now being challenged by scientists as a result of new discoveries and information gathered from within their own scientific disciplines. I also wonder whether we can afford the luxury of separating the knowledge about our physical material world from that of the world of the human spirit. Surely the two are interlocked and interdependent? I fully agree that one discipline cannot be stretched to explain phenomena outside its scope, but we get a very one-sided outlook if we rely on one way of looking at things. It is like taking a bearing, which will

[75]

be that much more accurate if it is taken from several different viewpoints, and the greater the convergence, the more trustworthy the result. As Paul wrote: 'Now we only see through a glass darkly' – but surely our aim must be to understand completely. And that requires a whole view of man and of our world, to which individual theories will contribute their insights, but all of which will need to interlock and support each other.

However, you have quite rightly brought the discussion back to the crux of the matter. For me that it is, as you say, 'the God of the New Testament'. And as I understand that Gospel, it is summed up in a command to love God and to love our neighbour. Both of these commands concern human behaviour. The sort of human behaviour for which we strive demands a high moral standard, and that high moral standard can only be sustained by a deep religious belief. Among all the world's religions, Christianity, in particular, insists upon the importance of the individual and his personal responsibility, and that the exercise of that responsibility must be seen in terms of unselfish service to others. That degree of unselfishness can only be sustained by a deep belief in a God of love, and by the sustaining power of that love working through us.

MICHAEL MANN

Dear Michael,

There are two things in your last letter that I would like to take up. I don't want to be difficult, but I am not certain quite what is the difference between 'some scientists are now seeing theology as a means of shedding light where previously there was a murky darkness' and, as you put it, 'a God of the gaps', except perhaps that it comes from scientists rather than theologians. At any rate we agree that the 'God of behaviour' is far more important anyway.

The other point is the possibility of evolution, or better

natural selection, improving man's ability to be evil as well as good.

I think there are really two separate issues. I do not think that the ability of men to do evil is affected one way or the other by natural selection. The ability to do evil is part of human nature and it really depends on the prevailing moral standards and the philosophy of education and upbringing in the community. After all, children can be trained to do evil just as easily – probably more easily – as they can be trained to do good. The element which is liable to the laws of natural selection is the process of education, not the human nature of the individual. My estimate is that a community whose system of education had the effect of encouraging evil, even if unintentionally, rather than good, would be more likely to disintegrate and consequently to fail in comparison with a community successfully striving to encourage goodness. However, the choice of system is still open to every generation and, as we agreed, people are reluctant to learn from past mistakes so that even if a particular system is a proved success there is no guarantee that it will always be adopted in future.

The other issue is the generalization about 'man' in this context. It would not really be right or just to blame the concentration camps on 'modern man' or on all Germans or all Russians. The evil, in this case, was done by individual men who lacked proper moral training or who rejected normal morality or, in the case of Stalin, adopted the Marxist morality of the end justifying the means.

You suggest that improvement through evolution tends to be material rather than moral. It is perfectly true that there has been much greater and faster material development in the last few hundred years than in the previous two or three thousand years, but until that happened practically all human improvements were in the realm of ideas and philosophies with the emphasis far more on civilized behaviour than on material improvement. Until the materialist explosion, the greatest influence on human existence was the gradual development of

[77]

increasingly sophisticated religions and philosophies, including particularly the idea of the Old Testament and of the ancient Greek and Roman writers. What have come down to us are largely the successful and benign ideas while the malignant ideas have either been forgotten or rejected as they proved to be failures in practice.

But surely modern materialism has not been entirely evil. Improvements in comfort, public health, opportunities to study and to develop leisure occupations at least are on the plus side. Furthermore, in spite of the increased potential for violence and evil in the contemporary world and of the provocation of terrorists and criminals, the general level of official brutality, in the more civilized countries at least, is lower than it was, say, 100 years ago and a good deal lower than 300 years ago.

To go back to the original discussion: I would say that we are not entirely of one mind about Darwin's theory of the evolution of species through natural selection. Although I entirely accept that it does not explain the origin of life, it does suggest the method by which species have evolved. Whether God is required to provide the origin of life permanently or temporarily until some further discoveries are made remains uncertain. Certain however is that God is very necessary to influence human behaviour as human nature is like to continue to have the same potential for good as well as evil.

I think we are agreed that human institutions and material activities are liable to the laws of natural selection but that each generation is reluctant to learn the lessons of the past except when it comes to making money or in matters of material comfort and convenience.

PHILIP

Sir,

I think that your letter sums up 'the state of play' admirably. I accept that modern materialism has brought immense benefits to mankind, for which we should be only too thankful. I would go so far as to say that we probably spend far too much time moaning that 'fings ain't what they used to be', and not enough time being thankful for the blessings of our material world.

The only point I have difficulty in accepting – because I believe that the evidence goes against it – is the suggestion that all man needs to be morally perfect is better training and a better environment. I believe that man has within himself a natural propensity towards evil, just as he has a natural inclination towards good, and it is this innate dual propensity that is both Man's triumph and his tragedy. As St Paul said: 'The good that I would do, I do not, and the evil that I would not, that I do.'

MICHAEL MANN

Dear Michael,

Could I add one final word to the discussion? I just want to make it clear that I am not one of those who believe that 'all man needs to be morally perfect is better training and a better environment'. All I said in effect was that a community whose institutions, including schools, were based on Christian principles was more likely to succeed, or, at any rate, would be more satisfactory than one which deliberately encouraged 'evil'.

PHILIP